Richard Scarry's
What People Do
Storybook

Random House New York

This is Busytown.
My, what a nice town!

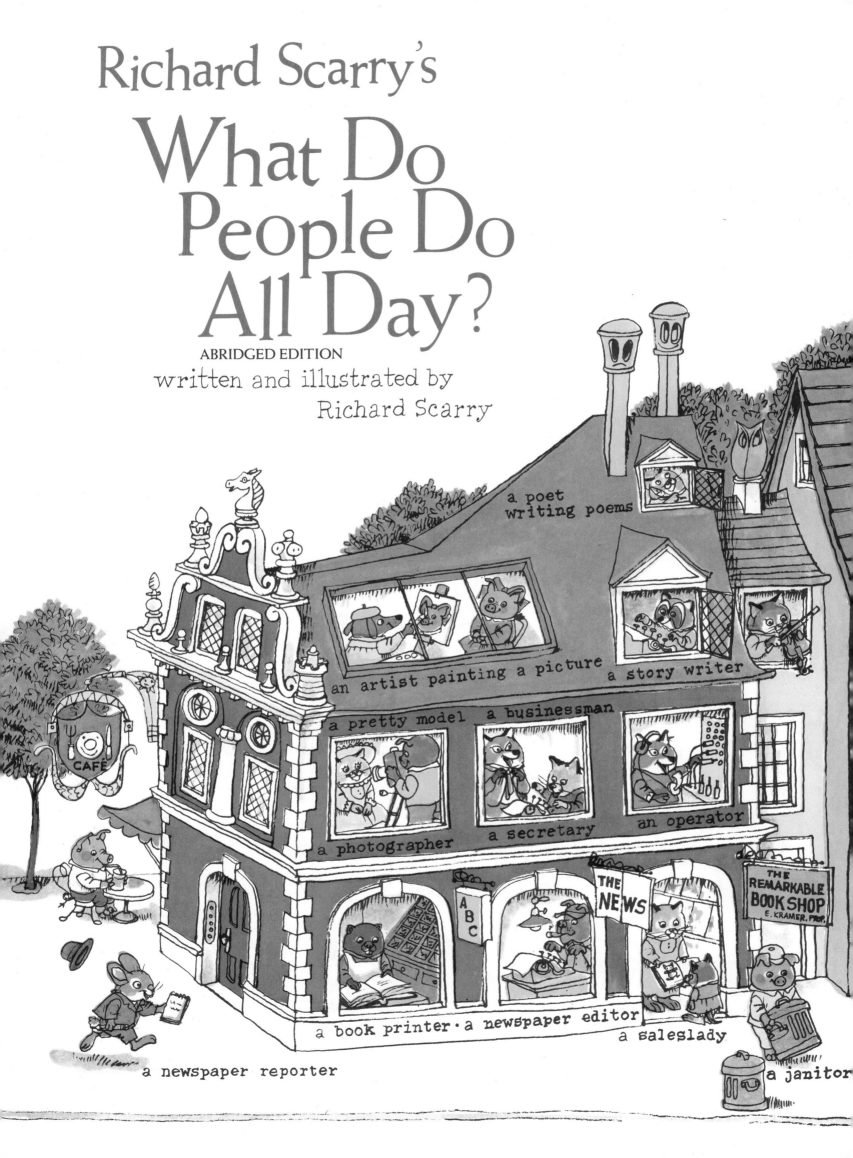

Richard Scarry's
What Do People Do All Day?

ABRIDGED EDITION

written and illustrated by
Richard Scarry

FINISH YOUR MEALS!

Wrong Way Roger

chimney sweep

dentist

doctor

eye doctor

dressmaker

beauty parlor

real estate office

music teacher

DANCING SCHOOL

BANK

DRUG STORE

PRESCRIPTIONS

street cleaner

Some workers work indoors and some work outdoors. Some work up in the sky and some work underground.

water hydrant

sewer

manhole cover

manhole

wire cable

BUS STOP

lamppost

sewage pipe

TO SEWAGE PLANT

All kinds of pipes and wires are buried underground

a stuck truck

a sleeping fireman

FIRE HOUSE

RITZ APARTMENTS

HARDWARE

window washer

BARBER SHOP

laundress

delivery boy

AUTOMOBILES

automobile salesman

Some workers always do their
work at the same place.

TELEPHONE
BOOTH

Others travel from place
to place to do their jobs.
What does your Daddy do?
What does your Mommy do?

TAXI

jack
hammer

And what do YOU do?
Are you a good helper?

ditch digger

Everyone is a worker

Farmer Alfalfa

Blacksmith Fox

Stitches
the tailor

Grocer Cat   Mommy   Huckle

How many workers are there here?
One, two, three, four, five, six.
What do these workers do?

Hi Daddy!

Farmer Alfalfa grows all kinds of food.
He keeps some of it for his family.

He sells the rest to Grocer Cat
in exchange for money.
Grocer Cat will sell the food
to other people in Busytown.

GROCERIES

Potatoes

Today Alfalfa bought a new suit
with some of the money he got
from Grocer Cat.
Stitches, the tailor, makes clothes.
Alfalfa bought his new suit from Stitches.

Then Alfalfa went to Blacksmith Fox's
shop. He had saved enough money
to buy a new tractor. The new tractor
will make his farm work easier.
With it he will be able to grow
more food than he could grow before.
He also bought some presents for
Mommy and his son, Alfred.

Alfalfa put the rest of the money
in the bank for safekeeping.
Then he drove home to his family.

Mommy loved her new earrings.
Alfred loved his present, too.

What did the other workers do with the money they earned?

First they bought food to eat and clothes to wear.
Then, they put some of the money in the bank. Later they will use the money in the bank to buy other things.

What else did they buy?
Stitches bought an egg beater so that his family could make fudge.
Try not to get any on your new clothes!

How do I look?

sand bag

bellows

forge

iron

Blacksmith Fox bought more iron for his shop.
He will heat and bend the metal to make more tractors and tools.

Grocer Cat bought a new dress for Mommy.
She earned it by taking such good care of the house.
He also bought a present for his son, Huckle.
Huckle was a very good helper today.

Building a new house

Huckle lived with his Mommy
and Daddy in a part of
Busytown where there were
no other houses nearby.
There were no other children
to play with.
Huckle was very lonely.

Then one day a man came and dug
a hole in the empty lot next door.
Someone was going to build a new house.
Huckle wondered if there would be
any children in the new family.

Jason, the mason, made a foundation
in the hole for the house to be built on.
His helper mixed cement
to hold the bricks together.

Sawdust, the carpenter, and his helpers
started to build the frame of the house.
Jason started to build a chimney.

I wonder if any children
will live there?

Jake, the plumber, attached the water
and sewer pipes to the main pipes
under the street.

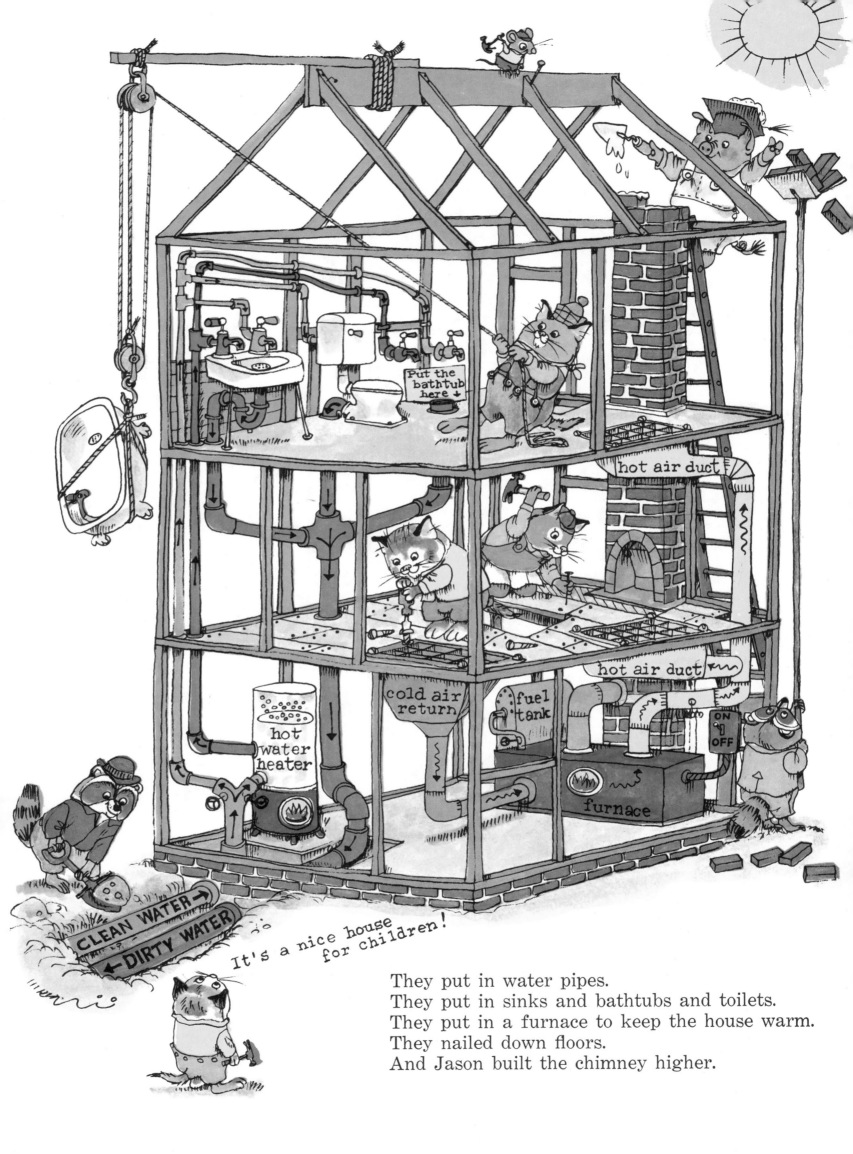

Put the bathtub here ↓

hot air duct

hot air duct

cold air return

fuel tank

ON OFF

hot water heater

furnace

CLEAN WATER →

← DIRTY WATER

It's a nice house for children!

They put in water pipes.
They put in sinks and bathtubs and toilets.
They put in a furnace to keep the house warm.
They nailed down floors.
And Jason built the chimney higher.

Jason finished making the chimney.
Be careful you don't fall, Jason!

electricity and telephone utility pole

fuse box

NEVER, NEVER
TOUCH!

They put a roof and sides on the house.
The electrician put in electric wires.
All kinds of telephones were put in.

The electrician attached electric
switches and outlets to the wires.

Sawdust nailed up the inside walls.
The walls covered up all the pipes and wires.

He put windows
where they belonged—and doors, too.

The house was painted
inside and outside.

clothes washer

stove

refrigerator

sink

A truck brought furniture, a television set,
a radio, rugs, pictures, a stove and lots of other
things. The house was ready for the new family.

At last the new family has arrived!
Look! It is Stitches, the tailor!
Stitches paid the workmen for
building the house.

bag of money

And here is Stitches' family.
"Look, children," said Mother Stitches.
"We have found a new playmate for you."
And Huckle was never lonesome after that.

Mailing a letter

Betsy Bear wrote a letter to Grandma to wish her a Happy Birthday.

She went to the post office to mail it.

She bought an airmail stamp and stuck it on the envelope.

She put the letter in the letter slot.

The postmen stamp all the letters with an inked postmark stamp.

The ink postmark tells you the name of the town that the letter was mailed from. The address shows where the letter is to go.

127,963
127,964

Uncle Benny, the postmaster,
read the address on each letter.
All the neighboring towns have
cubbyholes in Busytown Post Office.
Uncle Benny put all the letters
that were going to Grandma's town
in one cubbyhole. He put the letters
going to other towns in
different cubbyholes.

Then he put all the letters
that were going to Grandma's
town in a mailbag.

He took it to Busytown Airport
and put it on an airplane.

Off to Grandma's town the airplane flew.
A postman was waiting at the airport.
He took the mailbag to Grandma's
Post Office.

He read the address on each letter
to see to what part of town it was
to be sent. Each letter carrier
delivers letters to a different
part of town.

Soon the bag of Zip, the letter carrier,
was stuffed full. There was no more room
for the last letter, so he put it in his hat.

STOP! STOP!
Where is my birthday letter?

Sorry, Grandma

Grandma was waiting for a birthday letter from Betsy.

But Zip walked right past her house! He said he didn't have a letter for Grandma in his bag.

She asked him to please look again. So he did.

No! Sorry! No letter for Grandma. He tipped his hat "Good-bye" —and a letter fell out! It was Betsy's letter to Grandma!

"Why Zip! You dear postman!" she said. "You DID bring me a letter from my granddaughter after all!"

She was so happy that she gave Zip a big kiss. Grandmothers just LOVE to get letters from their grandchildren!

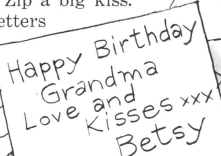

Happy Birthday
Grandma
Love and
Kisses xxx
Betsy

Firemen to the rescue

FIRE!
Mother Cat was ironing
one of Daddy's shirts.
The iron was too hot.
The shirt began to burn.
"FIRE!" she shouted.

Davy Dog went to the
fire-alarm box. He pulled
the knob that sounded
the alarm at the fire house.

Firemen are at the fire house
at all times. They have to be
ready to put fires out quickly.

As soon as the alarm rang,
they ran to their fire engines.
HURRY!

Clang! Clang! Clang!
The firemen rushed to the fire.
They raised the ladder on the ladder truck.
A fireman ran up the ladder to rescue Mommy.
"SAVE MY HUCKLE!" she screamed.

water hydrant

Save Huckle too!

Water is used to put fires out.
The water runs through pipes under the street.
The firemen attached a hose between the
water hydrant and the pumper engine.
The pumper engine got water from the hydrant
and squirted it out through the hose nozzle.

But the ladder wasn't
long enough to reach Huckle
up in the playroom!
How will they ever save him?

"SAVE MY HUCKLE!" screamed Mommy Cat
as the firemen carried her down.

Smokey came running to the house.
He had a smoke mask so that
he would be able to breathe
in the smoke-filled house.
He also had a special ladder.

He climbed up the
fire-truck ladder
as far as he could.
He reached up with
his special ladder
and hooked it over
the window sill. Then he
climbed up.
He just had to
rescue Huckle!

The playroom door was closed.
Smokey chopped it down with his ax.

He picked up Huckle—
and he jumped out the window!

PLOPP!
Sparky and Snozzle were ready
just in time to catch them
in the life net.
Daddy arrived just in time
to see Smokey save Huckle.

At last the fire was out.
Look at poor Daddy's shirt!
But that doesn't matter.
The firemen have saved
his family and his house.
That is much more important!

The firemen went back to the fire house.
They hung the wet hose up to dry.
They put a fresh, dry hose on the trucks.
They have to be ready to fight fires
ALL OF THE TIME!
Brave firemen are always ready
to protect us and our homes from fire.

A visit to the hospital

Mommy took Abby to visit Doctor Lion.
He looked at her tonsils.
"Hmmmm. Very bad tonsils," he said.
"I shall have to take them out.
Meet me at the hospital tomorrow."

On the next day, Daddy drove them to the hospital.
Abby waved to the ambulance driver.
Ambulances bring people to hospitals
if they have to get there in a hurry.

Nurse Nelly was waiting for Abby.
Mommy had to go home, but she
promised to bring Abby a present
after the doctor had taken her
tonsils out.

Nurse Nelly took Abby up to the children's room.

Roger Dog was in the bed next to hers.
His tonsils were already out.
He was eating a big dish of ice cream.

Nurse Nelly put Abby on the bed.
She pulled a curtain around them.
No one could see what was going on.

Why, she was helping Abby
put on a nightgown!

Doctor Lion peeked into the room.
He told Nurse Nelly he was going
to put on his operating clothes.
He told Nurse Nelly to bring
Abby to the operating room.

Off to the operating room they went.
Doctor Lion was waiting there.
Everyone but the patient wears
a face mask in the operating room
so that germs won't spread.

Doctor Lion told Abby that she
was going to go to sleep.
He said she would stay asleep
until her tonsils were out.

Doctor Dog put a mask
over her nose and mouth.
She breathed in and out.
In an instant she was asleep.

When she woke up she found
herself back in the bed next
to Roger's. Her tonsils were all gone!
Her throat was sore, but it felt better
after she had some ice cream.

Whooooeeee!
Abby saw her Mommy arriving
in the ambulance.
Abby thought her mother must be
in a hurry to see her.

Hurry!

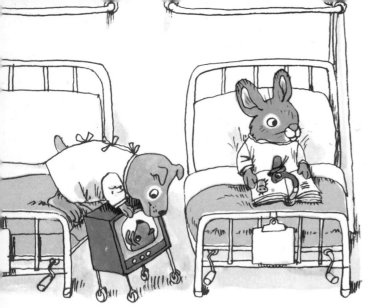

She waited and waited
—but Mommy didn't come.
At last Doctor Lion came.
"Your Mother has brought you
a present," he said.
He took Abby for a ride
in a wheelchair.

NURSERY

"There is your present," he said.
"It is your new baby brother!
Your mother just gave birth to
him here in the hospital."
Then they all went to Mommy's
room in the hospital.
Daddy was there, too.

What a lucky girl she was!
She left her tonsils
at the hospital,
but she brought home
a cute baby brother.

He looks like me, don't you think?

But remember! Very few children receive such
a nice present when they have their tonsils out!

The train trip

The Pig family is going on a train
to visit their cousins in a town far away.
They will travel all day and all night to get there.

Daddy buys train tickets
at the railroad station.

Mommy buys books
and magazines to read.

A porter takes their bags
to the train.

This old train has a steam locomotive.
It is only going to make
a short trip to the next town.
The Pig family will ride
overnight on another train.

Their train has a sleeping car
with separate rooms for each family.
These rooms are called compartments.
At night, the seats will be made into beds.
Look! There is Huckle's family.

Food and water is brought to
the kitchen in the dining car.
The cook will cook their meals.
The waiter will serve them.

ALL ABOOOOOARD!
It is time to leave.
The train rolls out of the station.
The signal light tells the engineer
that there is a clear track ahead.
He doesn't want to bump into another train.

signal tower

Mailbags and heavy baggage
are put on the train.
Some of it will be delivered
to stations along the way.

The locomotive needs fuel oil
to make its motors go.
The motors turn the wheels so that
the train can roll along the railroad track.

The switchman can
switch the train
from one track to another.
If he makes a mistake
the train won't go
to the right place.

The conductor collects the tickets. The tickets show that Daddy has paid for the trip.

In Huckle's compartment, the porter is getting the pillows and blankets ready for bedtime.

It is time to eat dinner.
Cookie has already made the soup.
He is trying to flip the pancakes
from the side that is cooked
to the side that is not cooked.
You are not doing very well, Cookie!

The mailman delivers a bag of mail to the railroad station of a town they are passing through.

The watchman lowers the crossing
gates before a train crosses a road.
He doesn't want any cars to
bump into the train.
But Wild Bill Hiccup
just HAS to bump into something!

Oh dear!
The train has swerved and the
waiter has spilled the soup!

While they are eating,
the porter changes
their seats into beds.

After dinner, everyone gets ready for bed.

Clickety clack, clickety clack.
The train speeds on through the night.
The train crew won't go to sleep
until the trip is over.
Cookie is still trying to learn how to
flip pancakes. Keep trying, Cookie.

SLEEPING CAR

DINING CAR

WIENER SCHNITZEL

ICE CREAM CAR

It is morning when they
arrive at their cousin's town.
Their cousins are at the
railroad station to greet them.
I think they will have fun
on their visit. Don't you?

The story of seeds
and how they grow

Farmer Alfalfa grows all kinds of vegetables on his farm.

Best of all, he likes to grow sweet, sweet corn.

Last summer when it was time to plant corn, Alfalfa poured the bag of corn seeds into the corn planter. Don't spill!

He planted the seeds in straight rows in his cornfield.

The hot sun shone down and after a while, tiny green plants popped up. The corn was starting to grow.

Rain fell on the plants. Soon ears of corn grew on the cornstalks.

Then—after many days of sun and rain—
Alfalfa opened an ear of corn.
He wanted to see if his field of corn
was ready to be picked.
It was! The corn was ripe and ready for eating.

Alfalfa drove his corn picker
back and forth across his cornfield.
The ears of corn were picked from
the stalks and dumped into a wagon.

Each ear of corn has many seed kernels.
Alfalfa knew that he would need seeds to plant
at the next corn-planting time.
So he put some corn kernels in a bag
to save for planting.
He kept some ears to eat himself.

He put the rest in his
little old truck to sell to Grocer Cat.
My! His truck is falling apart!

Well, that's the end of THAT truck!
Grocer Cat gave money to Alfalfa for the corn.

With the money he earned growing corn,
Alfalfa bought a shiny new truck.
The Pig family went to Grocer Cat's store.
Pigs just love corn!

They bought lots of corn and took it home for supper.

They ate and ate and ate
until there was no more left
—except one tiny little seed corn!
Mommy Pig said to Harry,
"FINISH YOUR SUPPER!"

Harry asked if he could plant
the last tiny seed instead of
eating it. Mommy agreed.
He planted the seed in the earth.
The sun shone hot and the rain fell cool.
After a while, a tiny green plant popped up.
The plant grew and grew and grew.

One day Alfalfa came to visit.
"My goodness," he said.
"Harry has grown the best
corn I have ever seen.
I am sure he will grow up
to be a very good farmer!"
Harry was very pleased.

Wood
and how we use it

We couldn't live without trees.
We get wood from trees.
We use wood in many ways.
Let's see how we get our wood.

TIMBER!

The lumberjack cuts down the tree.

The branches are cut
off the tree trunk.

The tree trunk is sawed into logs.

tree trunk

a seed

a one year old tree

This tree is almost 100 years old
and is ready to be cut down

log

The logs are put
in a river to
float downstream.

The forest ranger watches out
for fires. A forest fire
could burn down a whole forest.

Some trees are left standing.
Seeds from these trees
will fall to the ground.
New trees will grow in place of
the old ones that have been cut down.

The foresters also
scatter seeds from helicopters.

stump

Loggers ride the logs down the river.
They try to keep the logs from getting jammed.
Oh dear! The logs are jammed!
Unscramble that log jam, loggers!

Good work, loggers!
You broke up the log jam.
Now the logs can float to
the sawmill and be sawed into boards.

TOM SAWYER'S SAWMILL

Water falling over
a water wheel makes
all the machinery work.

lumber

lumberyard

SAWDUST THE CARPENTER

BOAT BUILDER

FURNITURE

The logs are sawed into rough boards.

The rough wood is sawed into boards of different sizes.

scrap lumber

FOOLSCAP PAPER CO.

straddle truck

This lumber is stacked in the lumberyard to dry.
Many kinds of workers come to buy the lumber they need for building things.
Daddy Pig has bought some lumber to build a bookcase.

The paper makers use scraps
of wood to make paper.

FOOLSCAP PAPER COMPANY

chipper

blower

digester

chemicals

beater

mixer

Wet wood pulp moves onto a wire screen belt.
Water is removed by rollers and dryers.

dry end   drying   paper making machine   wire screen   wet end   wet wood pulp

a finished
roll of paper

ABC PRINTERS

Some paper is used to make bags and boxes.
Some is for making books.
The paper used in this book was taken
to the printing shop where books are made.
The printer put the words
and pictures on the pages.

The boat builder uses curved
pieces of wood to make boats.

BOAT BUILDER

FURNITURE MAKER

lathe

jig saw

SAWDUST THE CARPENTER

FURNITURE

The furniture maker makes beds and chests and chairs.

Carpenters have a custom of nailing a tree branch to the roof of a new house.

Some trees give us fruit.

ICE CREAM

NEWS
GREAT Plumbing and Heating Problems at the Rotan house...
More later.

Trees shade us from the hot sun.

Harry is planting an apple seed.
An apple tree will grow from the seed.
It will take a long time.
Someday YOU might like to plant a tree.

Building a new road

Good roads are very important to all of us.
Doctors need them to visit patients.
Firemen need them to go to fires.
We all need them to visit one another.
The road between Busytown and Workville
was bumpy and crooked and very dusty—

—except when it rained!
Then the dirt turned to mud and everyone got stuck.

The mayors of the two towns went to the road engineer
and told him that they wanted to have a new road.
The townspeople had agreed to pay the road engineer
and his workers to build the new road.

Get rid of those bumps!
Make this road flat and straight, Bugdozer!

OK, Chief!

surveying instrument

BUMP

ROAD PLANS

The surveyor used his instruments to make sure that the road would be straight.

The grader makes the ground smooth

The motor crane lifts heavy things

The road builders used many machines to build roads. They put down big pipes to let streams of water flow under the road.

The bulldozer moves dirt

The surveyor's helpers used stakes and
string to show where the road was to go.

water drainage ditch

tractor
shovel

dump
truck

ditch digger

At last the roadbed was
straight and smooth.
But it needed a hard top
so that there would be no dust or mud.

Big rocks were put into the rock crusher
to be crushed into smaller stones.

A stone spreader spread the stones
evenly over the roadbed.

A truck squirted sticky asphalt oil
on the stones to make them stick together.

The stone cutter shapes
the stones so that they
will fit next to each other

sand pile

bucket loader

HOT ASPHALT MIXER

TAR TAR

TAR

The asphalt mixer made hot, sticky asphalt.

dump truck

level finisher

roller

The asphalt was poured into the level finisher, which spread it out flat on the road.

A heavy roller pressed down the asphalt to make it smooth and hard.

A GOOD ROAD

The road was built high in the middle so that rain water would roll off into ditches at the sides.

How am I doing, chief?

Street lights were put up so that drivers could see the road clearly at night.

FIREFLY LIGHTING COMPANY

electric cable

SNACK BAR

EAT

GASOLINE

gas pump

DIVIDING LINE PAINTER

gasoline storage tank

GAS AND OIL

OIL OIL OIL
OIL OIL OIL

GARDENER

All right, you two fellows! Stop talking and finish covering up that underground gasoline storage tank!

The workers put up guard rails
to keep cars from going off the road.

They posted many signs.
Some signs remind drivers to drive safely.
Some signs show which way to go.

STOP   NO ENTRY

SIGNS

A dividing line painter painted a line down the middle of the road.
Dividing lines remind drivers to keep on their own side.

HELP PREVENT FOREST FIRES

Don't push!

Everyone wanted to be the first
one to drive on the new road.
But Grandma Cat was the first!
Wasn't she lucky?

My Mink

A voyage on a ship

the ship's painter

IRISH PENNANT

cargo boom

cargo winch

dock

KEEP OFF

NUTS

WATER

FUEL OIL

FRESH DAILY

EGGS

APPLES

BREAD

CHEESE

MAIL

MAIL

Captain Salty and his Crew are getting their ship ready for a voyage.
The ship will carry passengers to visit their friends in a faraway land across the ocean.

At last the ship is loaded with
the food and other things they
will need on the long trip.
Here come the passengers!

They have all bought tickets
for the trip. They give the tickets to the
purser before they can go aboard the ship. NO PUSHING PLEASE!

light buoy

Tooooooooooot!
It is sailing time. A tiny tugboat pushes
the big ocean liner away from the pier.
Bon voyage! The big ship sails out of the harbor.

Soon it is crossing the wide ocean.
There is no land in sight.
Just look at all the things that
happen on an ocean-going ship!

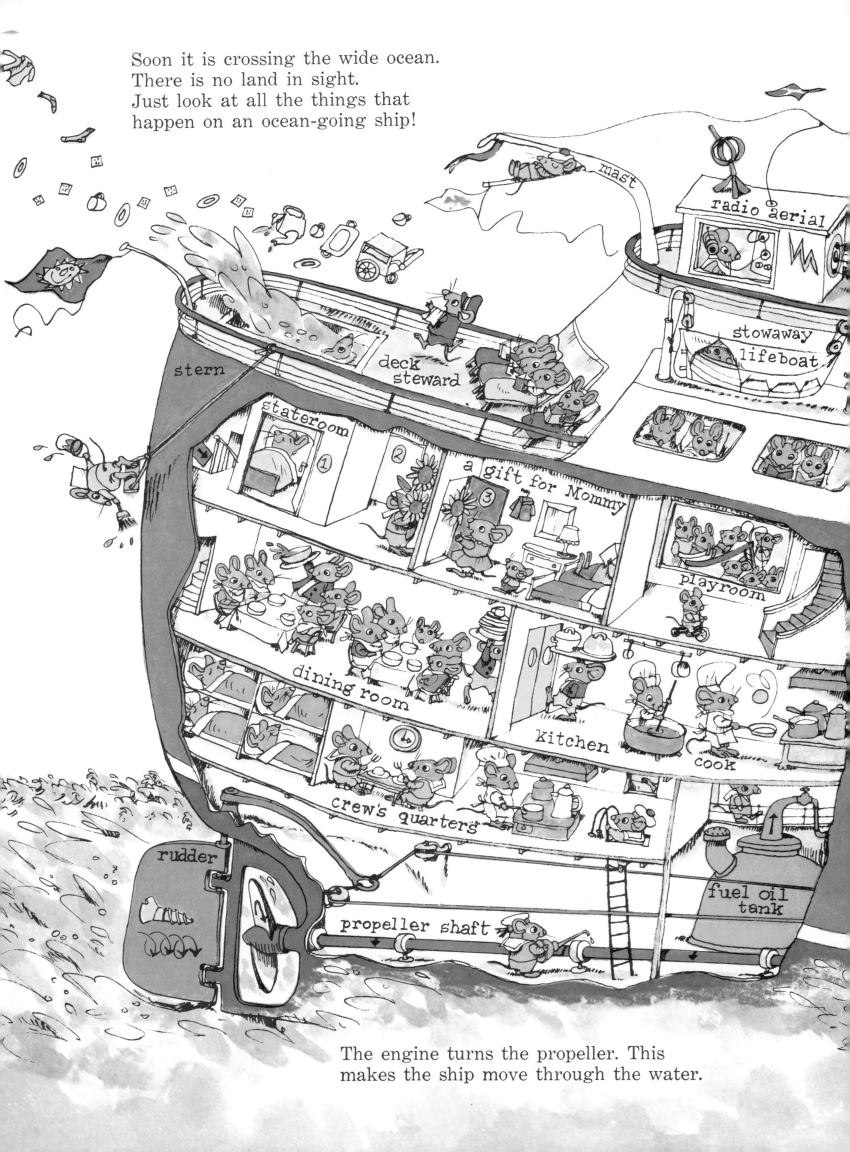

mast

radio aerial

stowaway
lifeboat

stern

deck
steward

stateroom

①

②

③

a gift for Mommy

playroom

dining room

kitchen

cook

crew's quarters

rudder

propeller shaft

fuel oil
tank

The engine turns the propeller. This
makes the ship move through the water.

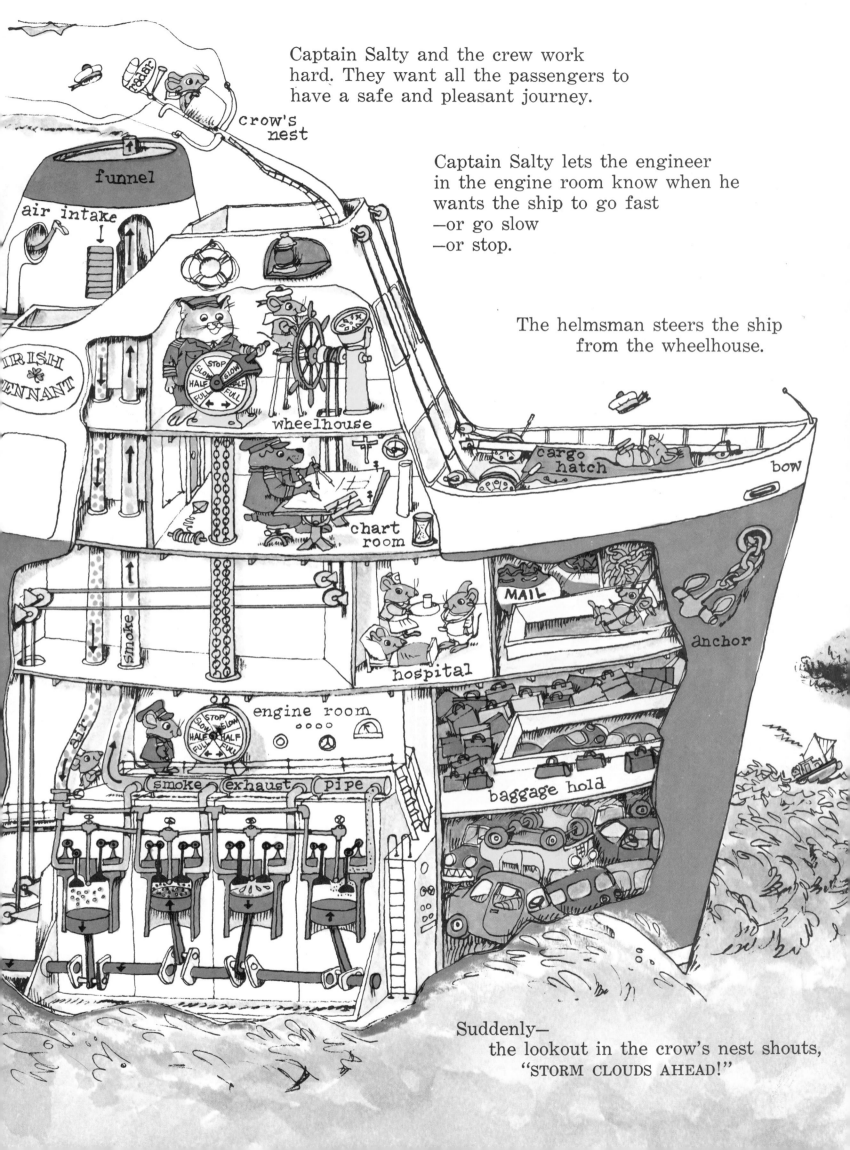

Captain Salty and the crew work
hard. They want all the passengers to
have a safe and pleasant journey.

Captain Salty lets the engineer
in the engine room know when he
wants the ship to go fast
—or go slow
—or stop.

The helmsman steers the ship
from the wheelhouse.

crow's nest

funnel

air intake

IRISH PENNANT

wheelhouse

chart room

cargo hatch

bow

hospital

MAIL

anchor

smoke

engine room

air

smoke exhaust pipe

baggage hold

Suddenly—
the lookout in the crow's nest shouts,
"STORM CLOUDS AHEAD!"

The storm hits the ship with great fury!
The radio operator hears someone calling
on the radio.
"SOS! HELP! SAVE US! OUR BOAT IS SINKING!"

Look! There it is!
It's a small fishing boat in trouble!

"FULL SPEED AHEAD!"
roars Captain Salty.
My, the sea is rough!

LOWER THE LIFEBOAT!
Hurry! Hurry! The fishing boat is sinking!
Sailors Miff and Mo row to the rescue.

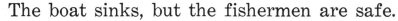

The boat sinks, but the fishermen are safe.

It's delicious!

LAND HO!!!

Back on board the liner, Captain Salty
gives a party to celebrate the rescue.
Will the storm never stop?

Then, just as suddenly as it started,
the storm is over and the sea is calm.
The ship continues on its journey.

Land ho! They have reached
the other side of the ocean!

Everyone thanks the captain and crew for such
an exciting voyage. Then they go ashore to visit friends.
Other people have been waiting to cross the ocean
to visit friends in Busytown. I wonder if their
voyage will be as exciting as this one was?

DEPARTURES
BUILDING

ARRIVALS
BUILDING

CUSTOMS
OFFICE

IN

TO
THE
BOAT

No pushing please!

Where bread comes from

grain combine

chaff

wheat field

wheat grain seeds

Farmer Pig gathers his crop of wheat with a harvesting machine. The grain seeds are separated from the stalks and poured into a truck.

bucket loader

The wheat grain seeds are scooped out and put into bags.

Then the seeds are taken to the mill.

FLOUR MILL

The bags are hoisted to the top of the mill. The miller pours the seeds into the hopper.

hopper

The seeds are crushed between the grindstones. Water power turns the top grindstone.

grindstone
turning stone
fixed stone

sharpening a grindstone

Sifters separate the soft flour from the hard shell of the seed.

sifter
bin
FLOUR XXXX
bran

The flour is sewn into bags.

FLOUR XXXX
FLOUR XXXX

falling water turns the waterwheel

waterwheel

FLOUR XXXX
FLOUR

The bags are put on a truck that will take them to the Bakery. OOPS!

FLOUR XXXX

The bakers will bake the flour into bread.

mixing trough

They mix water and salt and yeast with the flour to make bread dough. It is important to mix the right amounts. The yeast makes the dough puff up. The bakers knead the dough until it is well mixed.

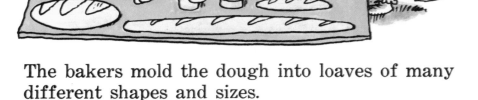

Able Baker Charlie mixes his own special dough. Isn't he putting too much yeast in his dough?

The bakers mold the dough into loaves of many different shapes and sizes.

Able Baker Charlie has made teeny tiny loaves.

Baker Fox cleans the hot fire coals out of the ovens.

The loaves are ready to be baked
in the hot oven.
The heat in the oven will make
the loaves puff up even more.

The bakers play card games while
waiting for the bread to bake.
Oh my! Look at what's happening!
Take out the tiny loaves of bread!

Too late! I think you DID put too much
yeast in your dough, Able Baker Charlie!
Mmmmmmm! But it DOES taste good!

Richard Scarry's

Funniest STORyBOOK Ever

Absent-Minded Mr. Rabbit

Mr. Rabbit walked down the street.
He wasn't looking at the workmen,
who were making a new, hot, sticky, gooey street.
No! He was looking at his newspaper.

He wasn't looking at his feet,
which were getting hot and sticky and gooey, too.
No! He was looking at his newspaper.

Then suddenly he stopped looking at his newspaper.
He looked down at his feet instead.
And do you know what he saw?
He saw that he was STUCK in that
hot, sticky, gooey street!

The workmen got a long pole and tried
to poke him out. It didn't work.

A truck tried to pull him out with a rope.
No good! He was stuck all right!

They tried to blow him out with a huge fan.
The fan blew off his hat and coat...
but Mr. Rabbit remained stuck.

Some firemen tried to squirt him out.
They squirted water at his shirt and necktie—
but Mr. Rabbit remained stuck. REALLY STUCK!

Well, now! He can't stay there forever!
Somebody has to think of a way to get him out.

Aha! Here comes a power shovel!
Let's see what it will try to do.

Well, the power shovel reached down...
and scooped up Mr. Rabbit.

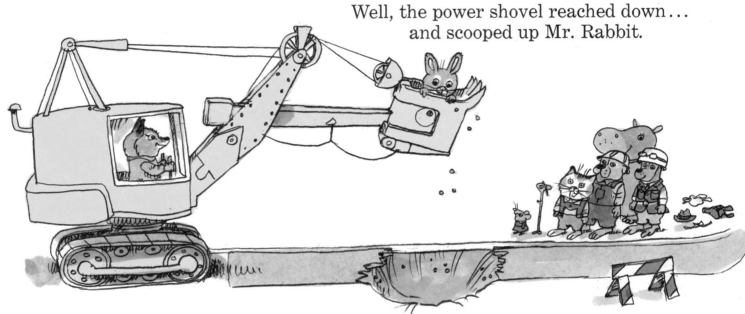

It dropped him gently to the dry ground.
He would certainly have to wash his feet when he
got home, but at least he was no longer stuck.

He put on his clothes and thanked everyone.
As he was leaving, he promised that after this
he would always look where he was going.

But a little while later he was reading his newspaper again. He had forgotten his promise. And, naturally, he wasn't watching where he was going.

OH!!! DON'T LOOK!!!!

Sergeant Murphy and the Banana Thief

Sergeant Murphy was busy putting parking tickets on cars when, suddenly, who should come running out of the market but Bananas Gorilla.
He had stolen a bunch of bananas, and was trying to escape.
    Murphy! LOOK! He is stealing your motorcycle, too!

    Sergeant Murphy was furious.
Huckle and Lowly Worm were watching.
Huckle said, "You may borrow my tricycle to chase after him if you want to."

B-r-e-e-e-t!

    Away they went... chasing after that naughty thief.

They raced through the crowded streets.
Don't YOU ever ride your tricycle in the street!

They crossed a drawbridge just as it
was opening to let a boat go through.

Bananas stopped suddenly and went into a restaurant.

Murphy said to Louie, who was the owner,
"I am looking for a thief!"
Together, they searched the whole restaurant,
but they couldn't find Bananas anywhere.

Louie then said, "Sit down and relax, Murphy.
I will bring you and your friends something delicious to eat."

Somebody had better pick up those banana peels
before someone slips on one. Don't you think so?

Louie brought them a bowl of banana soup.
Lowly said, "I'll bet Bananas Gorilla
would like to be here right now."

"Huckle, we mustn't forget to wash
our hands before eating," said Sergeant Murphy.
So they walked back to the washroom.
Lowly went along, too.

When they came back, they
discovered that their table
had disappeared.

Indeed, it was slowly creeping away
…when it slipped on a banana peel!
And guess who was hiding underneath.

Sergeant Murphy, we are
very proud of you!
Bananas must be punished.
Someday he has to learn that
it is naughty to steal things
which belong to others.

Speedboat Spike

Speedboat Spike liked to take his little boy, Swifty, out for a ride in his speedboat. Oh, my! Didn't Spike think he was smart!

Once he rammed into a sailboat.

Say! Why don't you look where you're going?

Another time he bumped into a barge and knocked a lady's laundry overboard.
(Swifty! Why don't you tell your father to stop being such a dangerous driver?)

Speedboat Spike just wouldn't slow down,
and he wouldn't stop bumping into things.

STOP!

But that was before Officer Barnacle caught him . . . and made him stop!

Officer Barnacle ordered Speedboat Spike to keep
his speedboat in a wading pool UP ON LAND!
Now Spike can go as fast as he likes,
but he won't be able to bump into anyone.

But who is that I see
in that tiny little speedboat?
Why, it's his little boy, Swifty!
Oh dear! I think we are going to need
another wading pool.
Go get him, Officer Barnacle!

Ma Pig's New Car

Pa Pig bought a new car to give
to Ma Pig on her birthday.
She will certainly be surprised
when she sees her new car, won't she?

On the way home, Pa stopped at a drugstore.
When he came out, he got into a jeep by mistake.
(You should be wearing your glasses, Pa Pig!)
Harry and Sally thought that Pa had swapped cars with a soldier.

Stop, thief!

Then he went to the supermarket.
When he came out he got into a police car.
"You made a good swap, Daddy," said Harry.
But Pa wasn't listening...and he didn't seem to be
thinking very well either. Don't you agree?

Next he drove to a fruit stand to buy some apples.
When he left he took Farmer Fox's tractor.
My, but Pa is absent-minded, isn't he?
    "Ma will certainly like her new tractor,"
said Sally to Harry.

They stopped to watch a fire.
When the fire was out they left—
in the fire engine!
How can *anyone* make so many mistakes?

Then they stopped to watch some workers
who were digging a big hole in the ground.
No! Pa did NOT get into that dump truck.
    But by mistake, he got into...

*Hey, Joe!
You forgot
to turn off
the motor.*

...Roger Rhino's power shovel!
Ma Pig was certainly surprised to see her new CAR!
But, Pa! Do you know how to stop it?

Yes, he did!

Oh, oh! Here comes Roger now.
He has found Ma Pig's new car
and is bringing it to her.
It looks as though he is very angry
with that someone who took his power shovel.

ROGER! PLEASE BE CAREFUL! You are squeezing
Ma's little car just a little bit too tightly.
Well, let's all hope that Pa Pig will never
again make *that* many mistakes in one day!

Mr. Fixit

Mr. Fixit can fix ANYTHING.
At least that is what he once told me.

He fixed the wheel on Philip's wagon.

He fixed Mrs. Pussycat's automobile.

He fixed Sam's boat so that
it wouldn't ever leak again.
My, that was a leaky boat!

He fixed the flat tire
on the school bus.
Don't you think that you
should stop now, Mr. Fixit?

He also fixed a broken street lamp.
What's the matter with Doctor Bones?
Can't he see where he's going?

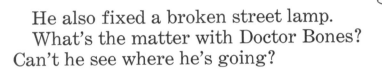

Dadda!

Mary's talking doll couldn't
say "Mamma" any more.
Mr. Fixit fixed it.
Now it says "Dadda."

He fixed Mother Cat's vacuum
cleaner, but he made a little
mistake.
It won't vacuum the floor
any more. Only the ceiling!
Mr. Fixit told her that she was
lucky to be the only one with
a vacuum cleaner like that!

He fixed Lowly Worm's shoe.
"You are a genius," said Lowly.
"I'll bet that there isn't anything
that you can't fix."
   "You are right, Lowly," said
Mr. Fixit. "I can fix anything!"

Then Mr. Fixit went home for supper.
After his wife kissed him, she said,
"Will you please give Little Fixit
his bottle while I am fixing supper?"
   Mr. Fixit filled the baby bottle
with milk. BUT... he didn't know
how to fix the nipple on the top.

He tried and he tried, but he couldn't
get it on. What a mess he was making!

Little Fixit said, "Daddy, let me try."
"It *can't* be done," said Mr. Fixit.
But he let Little Fixit try anyhow.
And Little Fixit fixed it—

on the very first try!

"WHY, THAT'S AMAZING!" said Mr. Fixit.
"Show *me* how to do it."
   Now, just be patient, Mr. Fixit.
Let him finish his bottle first
and then he will show you how.

The Three Sitters

Mother Bear saw Wolfgang, Benny, and Harry
walking by. She ran out and said, "My house
is a mess. I've got to clean it from top
to bottom. Will you please baby-sit with Robert
while I go shopping for some soap?"

Wolfgang, Benny, and Harry all agreed to stay
and play with Robert while Mother Bear was shopping.

After a while they got tired of playing.
"I have a good idea," said Harry. "Let's make
some fudge."
(I don't think Mother Bear would approve of that,
do you?)

When they had finished
mixing everything together,
they poured it into a pan.
(Do you suppose they *really*
know how to make fudge?)

Then they all sat down at the kitchen
table to wait for the fudge to cook.
Gurgle, burble! Burble, gurgle!
Something seems to be bubbling over!

POP!!!!
The oven door burst open.
The fudge had exploded!
RUN! RUN FOR YOUR LIVES!

Lowly ran to the telephone.
"HELP!" he cried. "The fudge is rising!
Our house is sinking in fudge!"

Look out, everyone! Here come the firemen now.
My, they are quick.

But, Lowly, WAIT!
Don't turn on the water hydrant
until the firemen attach the big hose to it.

Soon every bit of fudge had been washed
out of the house—along with a few other things.
But LOOK! Who is that coming?
Why, it's Mother Bear. Hurry up, fellows!
Straighten the house before she gets home.
Put everything back in place.

And hurry up they did!

"I have never seen my house looking so spic
and span," said Mother Bear. "I think we should
have a party. Who would like to make some fudge?"

Lowly spoke right up. "I think it would be
better if you made it, Mother Bear."

And so she did. And everyone ate the best fudge
in the cleanest, spic-est, span-est house ever!

Tanglefoot

Tanglefoot was going to the
supermarket to buy a can
of soup for his mother.
She told him to be careful
not to trip or fall.
"I never trip or fall,"
said Tanglefoot.

1
one   He tripped and fell
out the front door.

2
two   He tumbled over
a baby carriage.

3
three   He then fell into
the supermarket.

4
four   He bumped into the grocer.

5
five   He knocked over the butcher.

6
six

He tripped...and cans of
soup went flying all over.

7
seven

O-O-O-F! Big Hilda was in his way.

"I must stop tripping
and falling," he said
to himself.

8
eight

But then he fell over
the check-out counter.

He walked home without tripping
once. Very good, Tanglefoot!
He even helped his mother make a
big bowl of soup for supper.

9
nine

But when she poured it
into a big bowl, he fell
into it!
Tanglefoot said, "I don't
think I can trip and fall
once more today."

10
ten

But he did!

Good night, Tanglefoot.
Sleep tight.

The Talking Bread

Humperdink, the baker, was mixing
bread dough with the help of Able
Baker Charlie Mouse. His little girl,
Flossie, watched them squish and
squash the dough.

After they had kneaded the dough by squishing
and squashing, they patted it into loaves of all
different shapes and sizes.

Then Humperdink put the uncooked loaves
of bread into the hot oven to bake.

After the loaves had finished baking,
Humperdink set them out on the table to cool.
M-m-m-m-m! Fresh bread smells good!

Mamma!

Finally he took out the last loaf.
LISTEN! Did you hear that?
When he picked up that loaf, it
said, "Mamma." But everybody knows
that bread can't talk.
IT MUST BE HAUNTED!!!

"HELP! POLICE!"
Humperdink picked up Flossie and ran from the
room.
"I must telephone Sergeant Murphy," he said.

Sergeant Murphy arrived in a hurry.

He reached down and picked up
the loaf of haunted bread.

"Mamma!" the bread said.

Mamma!

Murphy was so startled he
fell into the mixing trough.

At just that moment, Huckle
and Lowly came into the bakery.

"That is a *very* strange loaf of bread," said Lowly.
Stretching out, he slowly ooched across the floor toward it.

He took a nibble.
The bread said nothing.

He nibbled and nibbled until only his foot was showing...
and still the bread said nothing.

Mamma!

Lowly stood up.
The bread said, "Mamma!"

Lowly took another nibble, then stuck out his head.
"I have solved the mystery," he said. "Break the loaf open very gently, but *please*... don't break me!"

Humperdink gently broke open the bread and inside was... Flossie's DOLL!
It had fallen into the mixing trough and had been baked inside the bread.

Mamma!

Baby!

With the mystery solved, they all sat down to eat the haunted bread.
All of them, that is, except Lowly.
He had already eaten his fill.

All right, Lowly! Please take your foot off the table!

The Three Fishermen

Lowly, Huckle, and Daddy were going fishing.

Their little motorboat took them far away from shore.

Daddy said, "Throw out the anchor, Lowly."
Lowly threw the anchor out...and himself with it!

Lowly climbed back in
and Daddy began to fish.

Daddy caught an old bicycle.
But he didn't want an old bicycle.
He wanted a fish.

Then Huckle fell overboard.
Wouldn't you know that something
like that would happen?

Daddy pulled Huckle out.
Why, look there! Huckle caught
a fish in his pants!

Daddy fished some more, but he
couldn't catch anything.
He was disgusted.
"Let's go home," he said. "There
just aren't any fish down there."

As Daddy was getting out of the boat,
he slipped...and fell!
Oh, boy! Is he ever mad now!

But why is he yelling so loudly?

Aha! I see!
A fish was biting his tail.
The fish was trying to catch Daddy.
It is good that Daddy has a strong tail.
Now Lowly is the only one who hasn't caught…

Wow!

But look! Lowly has taken off his hat.
Do you see what is under it?
A FISH! Very good, Lowly.

Yes, there you see three
very good fishermen!

The Accident

Harvey Pig was driving down the street.
(Better keep your eyes on the road, Harvey.)

Well! He didn't keep his eyes on the road
and he had an accident.

Sergeant Murphy came riding along.
"Everyone get on the sidewalk," he said.
"I don't want anyone arguing in the street.
You might get run over."
So everyone got on the sidewalk.

And just in time, too!
Rocky was driving his bulldozer down the street.
"I'm very sorry about that," he said. "I guess
I wasn't looking where I was going."

All right, now. Keep calm, everybody!
Here comes Greasy George, the garage mechanic.

Greasy George towed away the cars, and the motorcycle, and all the loose pieces.
"I will fix everything just like new," he said. "Come and get them in about a week."

Greasy George worked and worked to make
everything just like new again.
Stand back, Lowly and Huckle! Don't
get too close to him!

Well! Greasy George was certainly telling the truth.
When everyone came back, everything was certainly NEW!
I don't know how you did it, Greasy George, but I think
you got the parts a little bit mixed up!

My cap!

*Calling Sergeant Murphy!
Your little girl, Bridget,
won't take her nap.
Hurry home immediately.*

Please Move to the Back of the Bus

Ollie was a bus driver.
All day long he called out
to his passengers, "Please
move to the back of the bus."

At every single bus stop, he would politely
say, "Please move to the back of the bus.
There are others who want to get on."

My, see how his bus is filling up!

But look there! The back of the bus is empty.
No one will move back. Ah! Here comes Big Hilda.
She will move to the back of the bus.

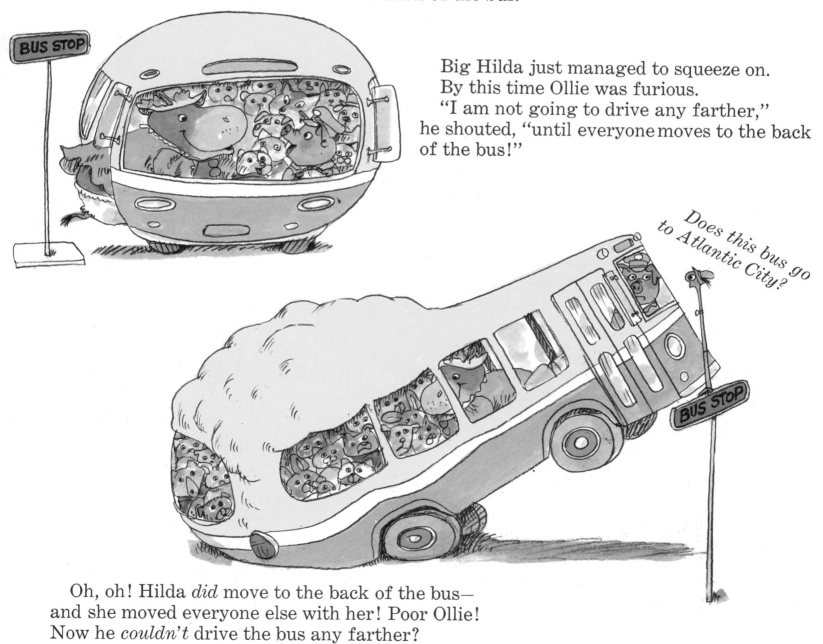

Big Hilda just managed to squeeze on.
By this time Ollie was furious.
"I am not going to drive any farther,"
he shouted, "until everyone moves to the back
of the bus!"

Does this bus go
to Atlantic City?

Oh, oh! Hilda *did* move to the back of the bus—
and she moved everyone else with her! Poor Ollie!
Now he *couldn't* drive the bus any farther?

All right. Everybody out!
This is the end of the line.

Uncle Willy and the Pirates

Not a soul dared to go sailing.
Do you know why?
There was a wicked band
of pirates about, and they would
steal anything they could get
their hands on!
But Uncle Willy wasn't afraid.
"They won't bother me," he said.

He dropped his anchor near a deserted island.
Aunty Pastry had baked him a pie for his lunch.
"I think I will have a little nap before I
eat my pie," said Uncle Willy to himself.

Uncle Willy went to sleep. *B-z-z-z-z-z.*
What is THAT I see climbing on board?
A PIRATE! And another! And another?
PIRATES, UNCLE WILLY!

But Uncle Willy couldn't do a thing.
There were just too many pirates.

First, they put Uncle Willy on the deserted
island. Then they started to eat his pie.
"M-m-m-m-m! DEE-licious!" they all said.

Uncle Willy was furious. He didn't care
so much about the pie, but he needed his boat
if he was ever going to get home again.

Then Uncle Willy had an idea.
He gathered some branches, some sea shells,
and some long beach grass. He wove the
beach grass into a kind of cloth.

Then he tied some sea shells
onto the branches and made
a ferocious-looking mouth.

He tied the grass cloth onto the mouth,
then attached some sea-shell eyes. By the
time he tied on a spiky palm leaf, he
had made a ferocious MONSTER!

Uncle Willy got inside.
He was now "Uncle Willy,
THE FEROCIOUS MONSTER."
Look out, you pirates!

The Ferocious Monster swam out to the boat.
The pirates were terrified.

They all ran into the cabin to hide.
The Ferocious Monster closed the door
behind them—and locked it.

The Monster had captured
the wicked pirates!

Then the Monster sailed back home.
Aunty Pastry saw it from the dock.
She was terrified!
   "There is a horrible Monster coming!"
she cried. "He is even worse than the pirates!"

Uncle Willy landed, and took off his monster suit.
Everyone said, "Thank goodness it was only you!"
Sergeant Murphy took the pirates away to be punished.

Well...Uncle Willy had made
the seas safe to sail on again.
Hurray for Uncle Willy—
   THE FEROCIOUS MONSTER!!!

How was the pie, Uncle Willy?

You BAD pie rats!!!

The Unlucky Day

Mr. Raccoon opened his eyes.
"Wake up, Mamma," he said.
"It looks like a good day."

He turned on the water.
The faucet broke off.
"Call Mr. Fixit, Mamma," he said.

He sat down to breakfast.
He burned his toast.
Mamma burned his bacon.

Mamma told him to bring
home food for supper.
As he was leaving, the
door fell off its hinges.

Driving down the road,
Mr. Raccoon had a flat tire.

While he was fixing it,
his pants ripped.

He started again.
His car motor exploded
and wouldn't go any farther.

He decided to walk.
The wind blew his hat away.
Bye-bye, hat!

While chasing after his hat,
he fell into a manhole.

Then he climbed out and
bumped into a lamp post.

A policeman yelled at him
for bending the lamp post.

"I must be more careful,"
thought Mr. Raccoon. "This is
turning into a bad day."

He didn't look where he was
going. He bumped into Mrs. Rabbit
and broke all her eggs.

Another policeman gave him
a ticket for littering the
sidewalk.

His friend Warty Wart Hog came up
behind him and patted him on the back.
Warty! Don't pat so hard!

"Come," said Warty. "Let's go
to a restaurant for lunch."

Warty ate and ate and ate.
Have you ever seen such bad
table manners?
Take off your hat, Warty!

Warty finished and left without
paying for what he had eaten.
Mr. Raccoon had to pay for it.
Just look at all the plates
that Warty used!

The lunch cost Mr. Raccoon
every penny he had with him.
"What other bad things can
happen to me today?" he wondered.

Well... for one thing, the tablecloth could catch on his belt buckle!

"Don't you ever come in here again!" the waiter shouted.

"I think I had better get home as quickly as possible," thought Mr. Raccoon. "I don't want to get into any more trouble."

He arrived home just as Mr. Fixit was leaving.
Mr. Fixit had spent the entire day finding new leaks.
"I will come back tomorrow to fix the leaks," said Mr. Fixit.

Mrs. Raccoon asked her husband if he had brought home the food she asked for. She wanted to cook something hot for supper. Of course Mr. Raccoon hadn't, so they had to eat cold pickles for supper.

After supper they went upstairs to bed.
"There isn't another unlucky thing that can happen to me today," said Mr. Raccoon as he got into bed. Oh, dear! His bed broke! I do hope that Mr. Raccoon will have a better day tomorrow, don't you?

Rudolf's Airplane

Happy landing!

LOOK OUT EVERYONE!
Rudolf von Strudel has fallen
out of his airplane, and the plane
might crash on top of you!

BANANA-MOBILE

Oh! *That* was a *great* place
for his plane to land. Wasn't it?
But how will they ever get it down?
The fire ladder is not long enough,
and I don't think *anyone* will
be able to climb up *that* high.
But there has to be *some* way!

Well Rudolf, at least, has landed safely.

Lowly and Huckle saw it all happen.
And Lowly had an idea for getting the plane down.
He told Huckle about it.
   "That's a good idea, Lowly," said Huckle.
"Let's do it."

First, Huckle broke a branch
off a tree. Then, with a piece
of string, he made a bow.
He was going to shoot
an arrow into the air.
But where would he get the arrow?

Lowly was going to be the arrow!

AOK!

Huckle shot Lowly into the air.
Up, up, up he went...

...and landed in the cockpit
of Rudolf's plane.
Lowly started the motor,
and the plane took off.

Does Lowly know how to *fly?*
Of course Lowly knows how to fly.
But does Lowly know how to *land?*
Of course Lowly knows how to land!

Well! I suppose that's
ONE way to land an airplane!
Very good, Lowly!

I think
I need
more
practice!

Lowly Worm's Birthday

It was Lowly's birthday.
Mother Cat was going to bake a birthday cake.
Father was going to town to buy some eggs
for the cake, and some candles to put on it.
And maybe a few other things as well.
  "Be careful you don't break the eggs," said Mother.

JOE'S HARDWARE STORE

BIRTHDAY
CANDLES
ON SALE HERE

Father Cat stopped at the hardware
store to buy some birthday candles.
HE LEFT THE CAR MOTOR RUNNING!!!
You know better than to do THAT,
Father Cat!

ONE WAY

Now! See what happened.
The car drove off all by itself!
I don't think Lowly knows how to drive.
Anyway, he certainly doesn't have a driver's license.

The car headed for the supermarket
to get the eggs for Lowly's birthday cake.
As it went past the egg counter,
Lowly picked up some fresh eggs.
Father Cat had to pay the cashier for them.

SOAP

SPECIAL TODAY! FRESH EGGS IN A BASKET

pickles

They drove out
through the back door
of the supermarket.

They passed Mr. Fixit, who was fixing a broken traffic light. Hurry up and fix it, Mr. Fixit, before there is a bad accident!

Don't be a litterbug!

Hang onto those eggs, Lowly ...and don't break any!

But where is Father Cat? Oh! There he is! He has just bought some balloons and favors at the party shop.

STRAWBERRIES

Through Farmer Alfalfa's hayfield they went.
I don't think Farmer Alfalfa liked that.
But then...it was the car's fault.
No one was steering it.

Father Cat was still chasing after them.
He stopped for a moment in order to buy
some of Mrs. Alfalfa's delicious fresh strawberries.
He thought they would look very nice
on Lowly's birthday cake.

At last they all came to a stop in Mother Cat's kitchen!

My babies!
My Lowly!

Lowly hadn't broken a *single* egg!

Mother Cat baked a huge birthday cake,
and guess who had the first bite!
It was Lowly's most exciting birthday ever!
Happy birthday, dear Lowly…Happy birthday to YOU!

Happy birthday, Lowly!

Mamma!

Baby!